GILES

SUNDAY EXPRESS & DAILY EXPRESS
CARTOONS

Sixteenth Series

A DAILY EXPRESS PUBLICATION

Published by Beaverbrook Newspapers Limited, Fleet Street, London, E.C.4, and printed by Purnell and Sons, Ltd., Paulton (Somerset) and London

4/6

INTRODUCTION

by

ADAM FAITH

I was very flattered when I was asked to write an introduction to this new Giles book. But then I began to have doubts. How can anyone introduce Giles? He needs no introduction. He is an institution. A part of the British way of life.

My own generation grew up with Giles. He was always there in our daily "Express", and a well-worn copy of his book was to be found in the doctor's or dentist's waiting-room.

And because he is an institution, I wonder how many of us have stopped to think that this world he satirises for us needs hectic hours of carefully thought-out technical ingenuity and thorough planning.

I would hate to count up how many hours of work and thought have gone into the compilation of this book alone. Although the very best satisfaction he could have must be the knowledge that literally millions of people will read it and love it.

When I make a record or do a TV show I hope that I am appealing to audiences other than teenagers. But with Giles there can be no question.

He is a hit with everyone. Every kind of home, every kind of person and every age group love to read their "Giles".

My home, anyway, at Christmas is incomplete without this book. I am sure it is the same for many of you.

For you regular fans here is another few hours of delight. And for you uninitiated (and there must be few)— HERE is Giles.

Adam Faith

"The Express is a bloody awful newspaper," said the Duke. "Ah, well," said Lord B., as they trotted him off to the Tower, "at least he takes it or he wouldn't know it was a bloody awful newspaper."

Daily Express, March 22nd, 1962

"Mr. Butler isn't the most with my 'Arry. My 'Arry was looking forward to being hung."

Sunday Express, October 15th, 1961

The Minister of Education, urging that *ALL* children from five to eleven should be sent to state schools, said: "Children of that age learning and playing together are not inhibited by any sense of differences."

Daily Express, October 17th, 1961

"However strongly we may feel about Sir Ronald selling us down the river, Miss Pummell . . ."

Sunday Express, October 22nd, 1961

Now there's an unfortunate thing to happen to a delegation of dockers on their way to protest about the gent who had his rates reduced because of dockers using bad language near his house.

Daily Express, October 24th, 1961

"A plague on you and your fall-out testers."

Daily Express, October 26th, 1961

"Well, well—at last—Jimmy Greaves hisself."

Sunday Express, October 29th, 1961

"That wasn't a fifty-megatoner or an earthquake—that was Grandma's tummy rumbling."

Daily Express, October 31st, 1961

"Keeping you and me back for another six months will scare the daylights out of the Russians."

Daily Express, November 3rd, 1961

"Whoops! Jock's trod on something sharp."

Sunday Express, November 5th, 1961

"That is a gross distortion of the facts—Mr. Sandys arrived home in the nose-end of a plane on his stomach, not in the tail-end of a plane standing on his head."

Daily Express, November 9th, 1961

"Here they come, Morgan. Don't forget—sorry we are to be so late,
minister's sermon was twice as long this morning."

Sunday Express, November 12th, 1961

"It's absolutely disgusting, dear, and I shall write to B.E.A. and tell them so."

Daily Express, November 16th, 1961

"You realise that by taking tea with graduates in their rooms you are liable to be rusticated, Professor?"

Sunday Express, November 19th, 1961

"Excuse me—I think you've still got one of my chaps over there."

Daily Express, November 21st, 1961

"How d'you like that—send us to Coventry because we got a rise and they didn't."

Daily Express, November 23rd, 1961

"In this ward we're trying this 'Floating patients on air' experiment you've been reading about."

Sunday Express, November 26th, 1961

"Give 'em all fire extinguishers."

Daily Express, November 28th, 1961

"As long as Madam appreciates that he's not a Viscount Linley and *I'm* not an Armstrong-Jones . . ."

Daily Express, November 30th, 1961

"They can put me in orbit anytime. They can put me anywhere they like except that Merry Christmas store where we work."

Sunday Express, December 3rd, 1961

"Oi! Just a minute, Maverick."

Daily Express, December 5th, 1961

"There is so little magic in the world. Let us encourage it in our children
as long as we can."

Daily Express, December 7th, 1961

"Fast as I tell him to 'See 'em off' they tell him to 'Sit'."

Sunday Express, December 10th, 1961

MERRY EASTER EGGS
MERRY NUTS
MERRY ASPIRINS
FESTIVE ROBINS
MERRY JUNK

"Miss! That was not the way to reply to Modom's request for a suggestion what to send her sister Millie."

Daily Express, December 14th, 1961

"If he ad-libs once more and says 'How goes it with the Three Wise Guys?' something's going to happen to that wire."

Sunday Express, December 17th, 1961

"Pity if he heard you refer to him as a dreary misconception of an obsolete legend—that's the general manager."

Daily Express, December 19th, 1961

"You go tell that judge that letting a man out for Christmas with his family is one thing—letting my family in to spend Christmas with me is another."

Daily Express, December 22nd, 1961

Daily Express, December 23rd, 1961

"Hold it, folks—listen to a recording made a few minutes ago of someone saying: 'Which do you hate most, his summer holiday films or his damn dog doing tricks?'"

Sunday Express, December 24th, 1961

" 'Morning, Sir—remember going home before Christmas in a funny little hat and kissing me under the mistletoe?"

c

Daily Express, December 27th, 1961

"I think Madame was most unfortunate to get a hair-blower
and five power cuts for Christmas."

Daily Express, December 29th, 1961

"And I say delivering your Scotch in time for Hogmanay or after is nae an essential service."

Sunday Express, December 31st, 1961

"We don't think Madam is remotely interested in purchasing a £15,000 yacht—
we think Madam has just looked in to thaw her tootsies."

Daily Express, January 2nd, 1962

"Go and rescue your father from the Sirens unless you want the house looking like Clydeside for the rest of the year."

Daily Express, January 4th, 1962

"Herbert—let off one more pigeon with a Pools Coupon while we're working to rule and so help me . . ."

Sunday Express, January 7th, 1962

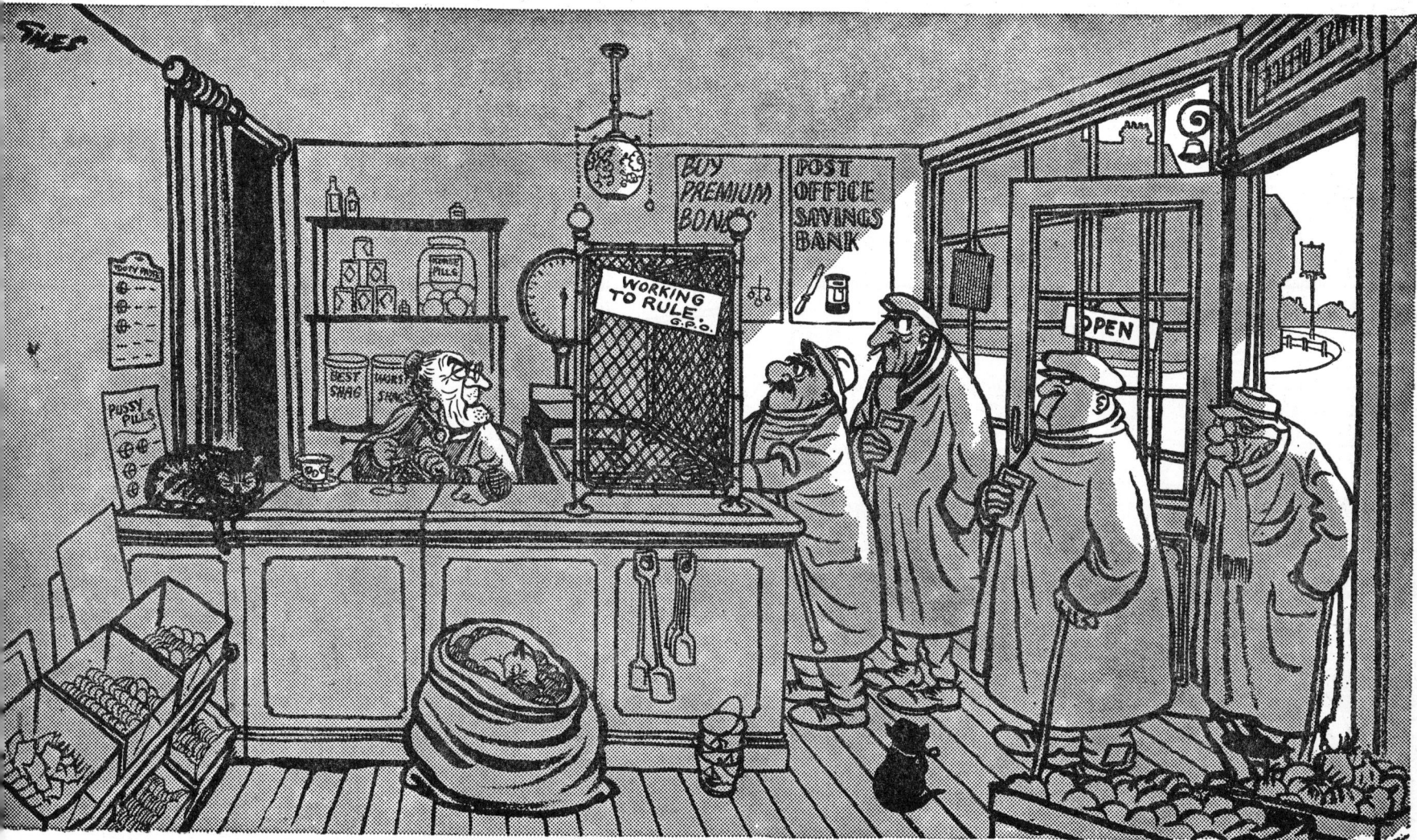

"Calling me an idle old faggot won't get your pensions any faster."

Daily Express, January 9th, 1962

"Forget the Go-Slow, Lilly—here comes that fast one from the stationery dept."

Sunday Express, January 14th, 1962

"Can't you see 'em—Common Market all the morning, Folies-Bergere all the afternoon!"

Daily Express, January 16th, 1962

"Mum! The postman's just brought that little salmon Uncle Angus sent us for Christmas."

Daily Express, January 18th, 1962

"If I'm going to have you hollering 'Mind my vaccination' every time I change gear all the way to Monte Carlo . . . "

Sunday Express, January 21st, 1962

"These remarks of yours: 'Smoke 60 a day'—'Drink $1\frac{1}{2}$ bottles of Scotch a day'—'Take Shirley Bassey to the flicks six nights a week.' We can assume you're joking of course?"

Daily Express, January 23rd, 1962

"Wotcher, Sarge. We've come to join yer."

Daily Express, January 25th, 1962

"With all due respect to the Archbishop appearing on TV with Adam Faith—
'Someone Else's Baby' and the Twist are OUT."

Sunday Express, January 28th, 1962

"The man who says he's going to sue the ref. for spoiling his afternoon's entertainment has started something—half of them have brought their solicitors and counsel."

Daily Express, January 30th, 1962

"The Duke says will it be all right if he borrows it next Thursday?"

Daily Express, February 1st, 1962

"I could understand you moaning about me bringing work home during the
Transport Strike if I was a keeper at the London Zoo."

"That note you sent the foreman the day they said the world was going to end—methinks he's reading it now."

Daily Express, February 6th, 1962

Daily Express, February 8th, 1962

"Do you know you're sitting on my Chihuahua?"

"Mother—remember you asked our mice to leave and they all moved in next door?"

Daily Express, February 15th, 1962

"Why do I think he heard you say you'd knock him off 3% instead of giving him an extra 3%? Because we've been here an hour and a half since you said it, that's why."

Sunday Express, February 18th, 1962

"In the last scene she gets snake poisoning."

Daily Express, February 20th, 1962

"During last night's celebration of Colonel Glenn's magnificent achievement no fewer than twenty-five men from this outfit signed on for astronautical duties."

Daily Express, February 22nd, 1962

"Please phone and ask Mr. Profumo if it will be all right if Michael Angelo here brings Augusta."

Sunday Express, February 25th, 1962

"May the Good Lord forgive me—'tis the first time I've said 'Top of the morning' to
Sergeant Murphy without putting a hole through his hat."

Daily Express, March 1st, 1962

"Since the announcement that more American women are enlisting in the Astronautical Service
I notice an increase in the use of cheap brilliantine and perfume."

Sunday Express, March 4th, 1962

"This bunch will be delighted—they've been looking forward to the pay increase to buy themselves out."

Daily Express, March 6th, 1962

"Grandma, forty cigarettes a day for the last sixty-odd years haven't done you any harm—why change now?"

Sunday Express, March 11th, 1962

"While you've been having your protest march most of them have slipped out for an emergency meeting in the Pig & Flute."

Daily Express, March 13th, 1962

"Matt Dillon's riding shotgun today, Sir."

Daily Express, March 15th, 1962

"Forgetting for a moment those of you who voted Liberal, there is one among us who went the whole hog—voted Labour."

"Another lettuce-leaf lunch like this and the Express'll be getting a series from me on 'How I killed my wife'"

Daily Express, March 20th, 1962

"Harry—didn't you tell the Guv'nor we'd dug an anti-doper trap over here?"

Sunday Express, March 25th, 1962

"You're out of his reach—ask him how went the Sport of Kings, yesterday."

Daily Express, March 27th, 1962

"This one's mine—up all night voting against more pay for nurses."

Daily Express, March 29th, 1962

"Dad—what's it worth if we don't tell Mum you've forgotten Mother's Day?"

"You appreciate that the one who put that slug through our local phone wire is responsible for wiping out the entire United States of America and half of Asia?"

Daily Express, April 3rd, 1962

"PHOOEY!"

Daily Express, April 5th, 1962

"Mine are just the same—nervy, irritable, difficult to live with—since they gave up smoking."

Sunday Express, April 8th, 1962

"Nothing to do with him giving up cigarettes and sweets—it's his mother."

Daily Express, April 12th, 1962

"Throwing potatoes at an Inspector while he's booking you for growing too
many during a shortage constitutes an offence."

Sunday Express, April 15th, 1962

"Five ton of best potatoes. My! You've been busy on the old kitchen garden, Fingers."

Daily Express, April 17th, 1962

"I suppose you will be spending three days of this joyous holiday beseeching that a pestilence fall upon the visiting team and the ref. be maimed."

Daily Express, April 19th, 1962

"*Who* had no right to punch his nose just because he walked on my wet cement?"

"It takes quite a time to get the knack," remarked the Prince, casually, following the announcement that Cowdray Polo Club wishes to encourage teenagers to play polo.

Daily Express, April 24th, 1962

"No one's going to convince YOU that all this is a waste of time now they've resumed H-bomb tests, is he?"

Daily Express, April 27th, 1962

"In case you've ideas about carrying 'em off 'Ban-the-Bomb' style, wifie's right behind you, Harry boy."

Sunday Express, April 29th, 1962

"Evidently the officer didn't think that whack round the legs with Marty's chain came under the heading of fun."

"Tom don't reckon his wages cover his European Language Mistress's salary."

Daily Express, May 3rd, 1962

"You take it round yourself, Nurse—I'm on strike in sympathy with yer."

Sunday Express, May 6th, 1962

"Never mind the Dook—GIDDUP THERE!"

Daily Express, May 8th, 1962

"Farewell, most beautiful chick this side of the Curtain—thank you, President Kennedy."

Daily Express, May 10th, 1962

"Pity you mentioned to Daddy that your young man happened to be
the Liberal candidate who knocked him off the Council."

Sunday Express, May 13th, 1962

"Last one out's chicken."

Daily Express, May 15th, 1962

ST. JAMES'S PARK

MP's OFFICIAL
BULLETIN
ON
PELICANS
DAPHNE   PAUL
(FEMALE) (DON'T KNOW)
ALL-NIGHT SITTINGS IN
HOUSE OF COMMONS

"Definitely a case for Sir John Wolfenden."

Daily Express, May 17th, 1962

"Little Miss Tinsel is one teacher who won't object to the Government's Child Minder scheme."

Sunday Express, May 20th, 1962

"They can't stay one inch off the ground for ever."

"Tell Acker Bilk he's got his first fan mail—from the people next door
asking when he's joining the Musicians' Strike."

Daily Express, May 24th, 1962

"The merry month of Maying . . . With a fa, la, la, and a fa, la, la
. . . And in three weeks' time the nights start drawing in."

Daily Express, May 29th, 1962

"One little rumble from Wall Street and away go our capital gains."

Daily Express, May 31st, 1962

The Royal Commission on the Police reports that there is insufficient readiness on the part of the public to help the Police.

Sunday Express, June 3rd, 1962

"I take it you want this certificate for your lumbago to cover the Oaks as well as the Derby?"

Daily Express, June 5th, 1962

"In the event of joining the Common Market how do you order two warm beers flat as ink in French?"

Daily Express, June 7th, 1962

"Messmates, hear a brother sailor sing the dangers of the sea."—George A. Stevens.

Sunday Express, June 10th, 1962

"Another weather forecaster who told 'em they were in for a non-stop sizzling Whitsun applying for asylum."

Daily Express, June 12th, 1962

"Now that the Germans are calling ye 'Poison Dwarfs' I want ye to look on me as a wee Snow White."

Daily Express, June 14th, 1962

"While I appreciate Dr. Ramsey's comment that preaching is an entertainment, I consider giving your sermon on a trampoline was taking the matter too far."

Sunday Express, June 17th, 1962

"A plague on this latest snob-craze of riding around in mini-cars."

Daily Express, June 19th, 1962

"Just tell me once more you and Harry have got the same outfits and you aren't moaning."

Daily Express, June 20th, 1962

"Next year we'll order a slap-up meal *after* we know the result of the last race."

Daily Express, June 22nd, 1962

"Bert's got a point there—if you're so keen on the express stopping here why can't you use your missus instead of his?"

Sunday Express, June 24th, 1962

"Private Evans, we find that receiving a letter saying your Gwyneth is carrying on with a Panzer Lieutenant in Wales is insufficient ground for bopping four German civilians on their hooters in Hamburg."

Daily Express, June 26th, 1962

"Now to find the Cinderella whose tiny foot fits this little boot."

"Proper hero this new leader of yours—with half the London coppers to protect him from little apples and a police escort to see him home."

Daily Express, July 3rd, 1962

"And I say your damn Wimbledon is interfering with my Test Match."

Daily Express, July 5th, 1962